Atlas of Butterflies
in
Highland and Moray

David Barbour, Stephen Moran
Tony Mainwood and Bill Slater

**Butterfly
Conservation
Highland Branch**

Highland
Biological
Recording
Group

this Atlas is dedicated
to the memory of
Jimmy Stewart DFC
1921- 2007

Published by
Butterfly Conservation Highland Branch
in association with
Highland Biological Recording Group

ISBN 978-0-9552211-2-5

Printed on recycled paper by

Big Sky, 305 The Park, Findhorn, IV36 3TE

01309 691641

Cover design – Bill Slater

Front cover illustration: Northern Brown Argus (Tony Mainwood)

Contents

Why not join Butterfly Conservation ?

Butterfly Conservation is the UK charity that takes action to save butterflies, moths and their habitats. You can directly support us by joining Butterfly Conservation. Annual membership entitles you to a colourful magazine, 'Butterfly', three times a year.

For more details about Butterfly Conservation's Highland Branch contact Jimmy McKellar –

Tel: 01463-241185 Email: jimmy.mckellar@btinternet.com

Butterfly Conservation Scotland – What we do

We work closely with the Scottish Government, Scottish Natural Heritage, local communities and conservation partners to safeguard Scotland's butterflies and moths, by:

- Advising landowners on managing land for butterflies and moths.
- Carrying out surveys of our most threatened species.
- Training volunteers to enable them to take action for butterflies and moths.
- Making recommendations to the Scottish Government on its environmental policies.
- Encouraging everyone to cherish butterflies and moths.

Scotland Office

Balallan House, 24 Allan Park, Stirling, FK8 2QG

Tel: 01786 447753

Email: Scotland@butterfly-conservation.org

Butterfly Conservation

Company limited by guarantee, registered in England (2206468)

Registered Office: Manor Yard, East Lulworth, Wareham, Dorset, BH20 5QP Charity registered in England and Wales (254937) and in Scotland (SCO39268)

Introduction

It is some ten years now since *Highland Butterflies - a provisional atlas* was published. Ten years seems a good interval in which to build up a new stock of records from which changes might be noticeable. The word 'provisional' in the original title was a nod to the fact that one of the aims of the atlas was to fuel a surge of new recording for the planned national atlas (eventually to appear as *The Millennium Atlas of Butterflies in Britain and Ireland* (Asher *et al*, 2001)).

Atlases of this sort are snapshots of our biogeographical knowledge of wildlife at a given time or for a given period. Just how 'provisional' atlases can be is borne out by the amount of additional information that has accumulated since 1998, and the changes which have been documented by this much augmented dataset. These new maps tell some encouraging stories of range expansion in some species in northern Scotland, although the notion that climate change might be a factor in these moves may temper our pleasure in them.

Back in 1998, the publication of *Highland Butterflies* was led by the Highland Biological Recording Group (HBRG), Butterfly Conservation's Highland Branch then being emergent rather than fully formed. In this edition, the prime movers are the BC Highland Branch and it forms a tribute to how strong the branch has become in the intervening years. Below, we have provided a brief outline of how we got from 'then' to 'now'.

Starting out

1987 was HBRG's first year of projects and included surveys of two butterfly species which were perceived to be expanding their range in northern Scotland, the Speckled Wood and the Orange-tip. The project gathered many new records from a wide public: however, the annual returns of butterfly records remained low until 1990 when Jimmy Stewart happened along and became the group's hard-working butterfly co-ordinator.

Jimmy had been photographing butterflies for some years and recording them in his own patch, Strathspey. He had devised a system of 'target maps', to monitor his own progress and guide future fieldwork, which he maintained on the plain sides of cereal packets! These target maps were ruled into 10km squares with one or two geographical features overlaid, and into each square was written a set of codes for the species recorded (either by him or from other sources). He provided customised maps to individual local recorders to encourage them too.

Jimmy fed the existing information from HBRG/IMRC (Inverness Museum Records Centre) and from Heath & Emmet, *The Moths and Butterflies of Great Britain and Ireland*, **7** (1) (1989) into an enlarged system of ten target maps for the Highland Region. As co-ordinator, Jimmy was a tireless correspondent and communicated on a regular basis with a growing band of Highland and Moray butterfly recorders. In 1997 his role as butterfly co-ordinator for the HBRG was taken over by David Barbour who was also the BC recorder for the same area.

1

The build up to the 1998 atlas

The collation of data for the 1998 atlas involved a varied set of sources. Some of them came from the butterfly recording sheets handed out by the Highland Branch of Butterfly Conservation or on general recording sheets issued by HBRG, but most came in as individually prepared lists - hand-written, typed or extracted from a variety of database packages. There were also bundles of single records on postcards, scraps of paper and telephone message pads which all found their way into the system. Lists were sent in by visitors to the Highlands in addition to the small band of resident recorders. The arrival of the RECORDER package at IMRC in late 1992 allowed the production of up-to-the-minute distribution maps for inclusion in newsletters and made the production of the 1998 atlas a viable proposition. Around eight and a half thousand butterfly records were entered for the years up to 1996, the product of around 166 recorders. It was difficult back then to exchange records electronically with national recording schemes, but these problems are now a thing of the past.

The analytical maps produced from RECORDER, using Plot5, allowed us to illustrate the patterns of recording in the Highlands. As expected, areas of intense recorder effort by keen individuals stood out in the midst of great open spaces where no butterfly spotters dwelt or ventured. The resulting coverage, therefore, was by no means 'blanket', but the scatter of dedicated recorders did produce some of the consistency required to monitor changes. For this reason we were able to have faith in the apparent spread of some species such as the Speckled Wood. A major task of the ten years since the 1998 atlas has been to redress that imbalance and become 'pro-active' in the gaps.

Butterflies for the New Millennium

The Butterflies for the New Millennium (BNM) project initiated a comprehensive re-survey of butterflies in Britain and Ireland between 1995 and 1999. This was run by BC in association with the national Biological Records Centre (BRC), the end result being the *Millennium Atlas of Butterflies in Britain and Ireland* (Asher *et al.* 2001). As a contribution to this project BC Highland Branch (in conjunction with HBRG) began to gather and collate records in earnest. During the first two years 1995-96, data gathered comprised 2202 records of 26 species, received from 66 recorders and from 43% of the 10km squares in Highland. By the time the national Atlas was published, 12,000 Highland and Moray records had been fed into the scheme – a massive effort in the context of the Highlands with its low recorder density.

Data sources for the Highland and Moray Atlas

The publication of the national atlas in 2001 served to encourage even more interest and effort in recording. The recording effort of the BNM project has continued to the present time, the interim results 2000-2004 being reported in *The State of Butterflies in Britain and Ireland* (Fox *et al.* 2006). In addition, monitoring along fixed transects, carried out under the Butterfly Monitoring Scheme (BMS) provides us with vital evidence of the fluctuations in our butterfly populations. 24 transects from this scheme are currently operated in

Highland and Moray, and the data from these have been fed into our current atlas.

The data used for the first atlas have been used in the current maps, having been transferred into Levana, Butterfly Conservation's own system for data handling. Records since 1996 have been entered directly on Levana and records from other recorders and sources have been fed into the combined database. The recorders credited in the acknowledgements (pages 4-5) are largely from the post-1996 period, the earlier contributors having been listed in the 1998 atlas.

It is important to validate, as far as possible, the identification of records which are included in the atlas. The last six or seven years have seen a digital camera revolution which has enabled large numbers of tricky identifications to be double checked by the sending of photographs as e-mail attachments. We can be more certain than ever before that what is included here has been subjected to rigorous checking.

Highland and Moray butterflies in context

Anybody looking at the distribution maps in this volume in isolation might acquire a rather distorted view of our local butterfly populations. Naturally, most of the species included are at the northern-most limits of their UK range, and folk might be forgiven for forming the impression that these species are distributed fairly evenly over the UK. This would be fair enough when considering the Small Tortoiseshell, the Common Blue or the Meadow Brown. Some species, however, have highly significant proportions of their UK presence in the area covered by this Atlas. The Chequered Skipper, Mountain Ringlet and Scotch Argus fall into this category. Other residents have the mainstay of their Scottish population with us: butterflies such as Small Blue and Dingy Skipper. The Small Pearl-bordered Fritillary and the Pearl-bordered Fritillary, generally flourishing in our area, are contracting their range south of Scotland. In fact no fewer than 11 of our resident species are among those now listed as 'Priority Species' nationally. It is evident, then, that what we have around us is an important set of butterfly populations which are highly worthy of our attention and conservation.

As the effects of climate change manifest themselves more clearly with the passing years, the north Scottish butterfly populations may prove to be particularly significant. If we continue to record their distribution in detail and over time, we can make informed guesses about trends and, more importantly, act intelligently to conserve them as a prominent part of our national fauna and flora.

Acknowledgements

There are various organisations and individuals to thank for their help in the production of this volume.

We would particularly like to place on record our debt of gratitude to Derek C Hulme, who was engaged on his own version of this work years before the first version appeared in 1998. He very generously gave us access to his notes, ideas and records.

Murdo Macdonald has assisted hugely in the devising of 'phenology generators' which have taken hours of toil out of chart construction. He has had similar inputs into the finished maps.

A number of photographers of butterflies have kindly allowed us to use their images to enhance and inform this volume. Their individual contributions are credited in the copyright section on the reverse of the title page.

Scottish Natural Heritage provided funding towards the costs of production and our thanks go to Ian Mitchell, Steve North and Fraser Symonds for their help and encouragement. Richard Fox kindly gave us access to additional records held by Butterfly Conservation. Helen Mainwood kindly helped with proof reading.

The most important component of this atlas is, of course, the 'recorder', more than 750 of whom have contributed their time and energy to making over 40,000 observations and contributing them to this atlas. The constraints on space in this volume allow us to name (and praise) only a group of the major contributors (50 records or more); to all who have sent in records, **THANK YOU**...and keep on sending more!

Tommy Archibald
Jane Arnold
Jim Asher
Rosemary Atkins
Barbara & Brian
   Ballinger
David Barbour
Donald Beaton
Clare Belshaw
Nigel Bourn
Bill Bourne
Jane Bowman
Peter Burr
Ewan Campbell
John Chester
Julian Clarke
J.S Clarke
Ray Collier
Roger Cottis
I R Cunningham
Margaret Currie
M Curry
Duncan Davidson

Sandy Davidson
Kevin Davis
Andrew Daw
R Dobson
Keith Duncan
Philip Entwistle
Jane Erridge
Ian M Evans
Robin Field
David & Susan
   Findlay
Richard Fox
Ian Francis
Aldina Franco
Sydney Gauld
W A Gerrard
Andy Godfrey
Peter Gordon Smith
Martin Greenland
Neil Gregory
Jean Hagley
Peter Hardy
Steve Hardy

David Hayes
Dick Hewitt
Rosemary Holt
Sue Hood
Jonathan Hughes
Derek C Hulme
M Innes
Hugh Insley
Sallie Jack
Phil James
David Jardine
Gus Jones
D Kennedy
Paul Kerrison
Janet King
Pete Kinnear
Paul Kirkland
Alan J Lawrence
M P Laycock
Mary Legg
Roy Leverton
John & Brenda Lunn
Murdo Macdonald

Liz Macdonald
Sandra Maclean
Peter Madden
Tony & Helen
   Mainwood
S Mason
David & Heather
   McAllister
Jimmy McKellar
Alison Mclaggan
Tony Millard
David Miller
Keith Miller
Pete Moore
Stephen Moran
Ewan Munro
Jackie Muscott
Brian Neath
David Newland
the late Gill Nisbet
Jane O'Donovan
Bob Palmer
S M Palmer

David Patterson
John Phillips
Richard Prentice
Tom Prescott
Neil Ravenscroft
Gwen Richards
Mo Richards
Colin Ridley
Adrian Riley
Craig Robson

Lynden Schofield
Andy Scott
Nick Semple
Bill Slater
Ann Smart
R G Smith
Anne-Marie & Chris
    Smout
Barbara Soutar
Richard Southwell

Alex Stewart
the late Jimmy
    Stewart
Julie Stoneman
Sue Tarr
Mike Taylor
Stewart Taylor
B R Tucker
Audrey Turner
John R G Turner

Jeff Waddell
Irene Wade
Heather Walshaw
Kenneth Watt
Lyn Wells
David Whitaker
Fay Wilkinson
Duncan Williams
Mark Young
Ron Youngman

Species expanding their ranges

One of the most fascinating aspects of recording butterfly distribution for this atlas has been to see the fast-moving changes in many species - some declining but others strongly increasing. Since 1995 several species have increased and spread in the region, and this is not really adequately conveyed by the maps in the species accounts, which are cumulative and so do not distinguish recent arrival from long-term residence. Here we are attempting to give a clearer picture of the patterns of spread for four species where it has been particularly dramatic.

Two of these species, Orange-tip and Speckled Wood, have been spreading in the north of Scotland for some decades. The other two species, Peacock and Ringlet, have arrived much more recently, since the year 2000. Climate change has been suggested as the reason for these increases, and perhaps knowledge of the detailed timing and sequence of the expansions may help to confirm this (or not!).

The two species showing long-term increase began to show changes several years before the start of the recording period of this atlas. For this reason we have drawn on older information on these, which is available through the National Biodiversity Network (NBN). Information from the NBN was incorporated into the maps and accounts of the expansion of Orange-tip and Speckled Wood in the period 1970-1982, to supplement our own records.

In comparing maps for earlier periods with the later ones representing 1996-2007, it should be realised that recording was less intensive in the earlier years, and some of the differences are attributable to this factor: however other differences, involving major colonisation of new areas, are reliably shown by the map comparisons. (Partly to offset this difference in recording intensity, the maps are plotted at 10km resolution rather than the 5km scale used for maps in the main species accounts).

Orange-tip

The Orange–tip was very localised in north Scotland as recently as the 1960s when it was more-or-less confined to the north-east corner of the country (Aberdeenshire, Banffshire, Moray and Nairn, and East Inverness-shire). In southern Scotland it was then long extinct, only re-colonising from Northumberland in the 1970s.

Our first map, representing the period 1970-82, shows that even by the start of the '80s it had spread little beyond its north-eastern core area, appearing in only a few scattered locations westward to Lochaber and Wester Ross. (Isolated dots in west and south-east Sutherland are believed to represent single sightings at that time).

The second map, 13 years later, shows a dramatic westward shift to Sunart and Morvern, to Lochalsh and Skye, and a considerable filling-in throughout Easter Ross on the other side. From what we know of this period, the westward jump seems to have been accomplished particularly rapidly, in the early and mid 1980s. The map gives an indication of at least three separate routes of spread through the central glens. It should be borne in mind that this spread happened at exactly the same time as the rapid colonisation of much of south Scotland by the Orange-tip, from an original foothold somewhere in the eastern Borders. The southern and northern Scottish populations were to remain widely separated for several more years.

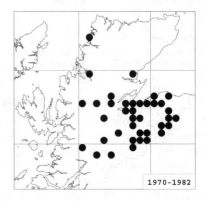

1970-1982

The third map in the Orange-tip sequence shows the up-to-date picture, and benefits from much increased recording. Not only the BNM project but two Butterfly Conservation Scotland-wide surveys (in 1997-98 and 2007) have given a particularly detailed picture of the Orange-tip's distribution. The further spread since the preceding period was mostly in the north and west, with some indication of a filling-in in central parts too. The 2007 survey found 20 new 10km squares in the region, and of these, 13 were on the northern or western fringes of the previously-known range. The species remains absent from Caithness and a large part of Sutherland.

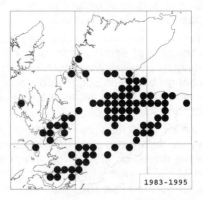

1983-1995

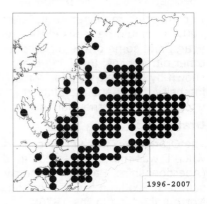

1996-2007

Speckled Wood

This species has shown an increase in our area even more extensive than that of the Orange-tip. Its spread to the east began in the late 1950s and the 1960s, before which it was completely confined to an area of the western seaboard (up to Skye and Lochalsh).

Our first map shows the eastern expansion already well underway, having spread through coastal Moray in the 1970s from a starting-point probably near Inverness. On the west too it had shown significant movement, the sites in north-west Ross-shire being quite recently colonised. The first sighting just into Sutherland came in 1982. In the intervening central area its representation was sparse, so for this species the route of the original west-to-east spread is something of a mystery.

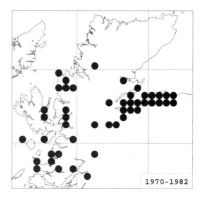

The expansion continued apace over the next 13 years. The map shows colonisation of west and south-east Sutherland in this period, as well as a distinct inland movement in Moray and Speyside. The central area, however, seemed still largely to lack sightings of Speckled Wood beyond Glen Affric, where it had been established for some time.

The third map (1996-2007) shows the most remarkable increase yet, the species turning up in north Sutherland (2002), Caithness (2005), and massively filling in the central area (Lochaber, Loch Ness-side, parts of central Ross) where it previously seemed absent. The impression of two distinct populations, east and west, no longer holds good.

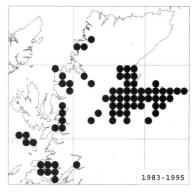

In the years covered by this map, it is worth pointing out, the Speckled Wood spread also into Aberdeenshire and founded colonies in inland Perthshire. Apart from Argyll and the Argyll islands, it has remained substantially absent over the rest of Scotland.

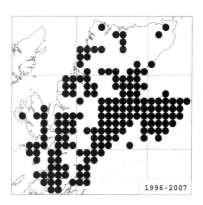

Peacock

Moving on to a species which has arrived with us much more recently, the Peacock butterfly was a rarity here right up to the turn of the Millennium. Our first map 1995-1999 (a shorter time-scale for comparison than the previous two species) shows the scatter-gun pattern of a sporadic migrant, liable to turn up as a one-off at any place but permanently resident in none. The Peacock was a common resident butterfly over most of the British Isles, but only up to southern Scotland.

This situation continued to obtain up to early September 2002. Then literally overnight (11th September) a huge influx of Peacock butterflies appeared through Moray and Nairn, East Inverness-shire and part of Easter Ross. The origin of these was believed to be migratory, and meteorological evidence (of easterly winds at the time) suggested they might even have been transported from the near continent. This was a very welcome addition to our butterfly fauna that autumn, but we could not predict whether the newcomers would stay.

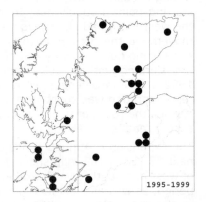
1995-1999

A smaller number of Peacocks appeared the same autumn in the south-west of Highland, but these were little more than a continuation of the trickle northwards of this butterfly from neighbouring Argyll (where it had been on the increase).

Happily, the Peacock was seen again in spring 2003, in all the same areas as in the September invasion. It bred successfully in summer 2003, and has been a regular quite common butterfly with us ever since. In a virtually unique instance, this single species colonised more than a thousand square miles of our territory in a single step.

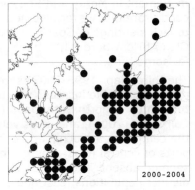
2000-2004

As the map shows, the colonisation did not extend at first to the extreme north or west. The situation there remained much as before, with scattered individual sightings that seemed to be no more than vagrants.

A third map, representing only the three years 2005-07, shows the final stage of the Peacock's spread. Though in 2005 the distribution was still much as it had been for three years, 2006 saw another major movement to the north and north-west, the

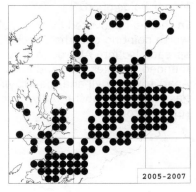
2005-2007

butterflies being seen commonly right up to the north coast of Sutherland. Allowing for sparser recording coverage in the remoter parts (in just two years of presence), this butterfly can now be said to be well established and resident over the whole of our area.

In distinct contrast to the gradual spread of the Orange-tip and the Speckled Wood, the Peacock colonised the whole of our region in essentially two giant leaps, over only a four-year period.

Ringlet

One other species has started to colonise this area since the year 2000. The Ringlet was, rather like the Peacock, a widespread common butterfly over most of mainland Britain, but reaching a northern limit in the fringes of the Scottish Highlands. Its extreme outpost of distribution was in lowland Aberdeenshire, where it had persisted for many decades. A general increase in central Scotland and Aberdeenshire was apparent by the 1990s, and consequent on this a small number of stray individuals began to appear occasionally in our area.

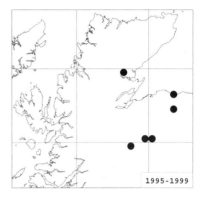

The first map (1995-99) shows this stage, where scattered generally single specimens were recorded at a few locations in the east. An exceptional instance was the single Ringlet at Spinningdale in 1996, far outside the known breeding range and demonstrating the potential for this species to 'jump' large distances although it is not generally reckoned to be migratory.

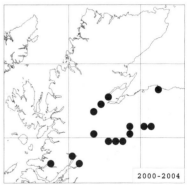

Moving forward 5 years, the second map shows a distinct change. Almost none of the 1995-99 sightings was repeated in the same locations, but a series of findings mainly in the upper Spey and Monadhliath areas began to establish a pattern of what was probably the beginnings of a resident population. The short distance from neighbouring Perthshire, where the species had been increasing and spreading, suggests the origin of this colonisation. A few scattered records came from places farther west and north.

2005 was really the year of major change for the Ringlet butterfly here. Suddenly it

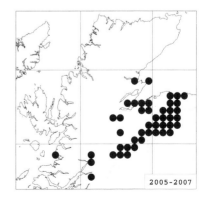

was found to be established quite widely in parts of central Speyside and upland Moray. It appeared for the first time on butterfly monitoring transects at Loch Garten and Insh Marshes. It was recorded at new sites as far apart as Portknockie in the east and Arisaig in the west.

In the two subsequent years, it has been possible to track the Ringlet's progress deeper into Highland. It has been found, sometimes singly and sometimes in numbers, at a large number of new sites in the south-east of the region. In 2006 an extreme northern colony, of moderate size, was found at Camore Wood in Sutherland. In 2007 a colony was found at Rockfield near the tip of the Tain peninsula. In the west it has been seen additionally at Glencoe and Fort William.

The map, indicating Ringlets in 44 squares in just a 3-year period, is striking evidence for yet another major butterfly colonisation in our region. This one has been not quite so sudden as the Peacock's, nor quite so gradual as the Orange-tip's or the Speckled Wood's, but it has certainly been rapid, and is continuing as rapidly at the time of writing (summer 2008).

These four species are not the only cases of butterflies increasing their distribution-range in Highland and Moray. Others have spread less dramatically, some just filling in former spaces within a larger range. Others show promise of colonising soon from outside the area. The Comma, which only recently re-colonised southern Scotland, has been seen twice in Highland and may some day become established.

All in all these positive changes seem to us to far outweigh the few decreases or losses that have occurred to butterflies here in the far north of the UK. Perhaps by an accident of geography we are enjoying a period of very pleasing increase in the species-richness of these, our favourite insects.

Explanation of the Maps and Charts

Priority Species - denotes a priority species in the UK Biodiversity Action Plan (UKBAP). Eleven of the species in our area fall into this special category; more than a third of our butterflies.

Maps - Each map has been generated using **DMAP (www.dmap.co.uk)** The dots represent 5km grid squares (except for the maps pp 5-10, for species expanding their range which are plotted at 10km size).

Phenology charts - The dataset used to create the weekly phenology charts is entirely drawn from the 1995-2007 period. Each column in the chart represents a 'quarter month' rather than a calendar week. Over 30,000 records from the butterfly dataset contained enough detailed information to be included in these charts.

Map of Atlas coverage

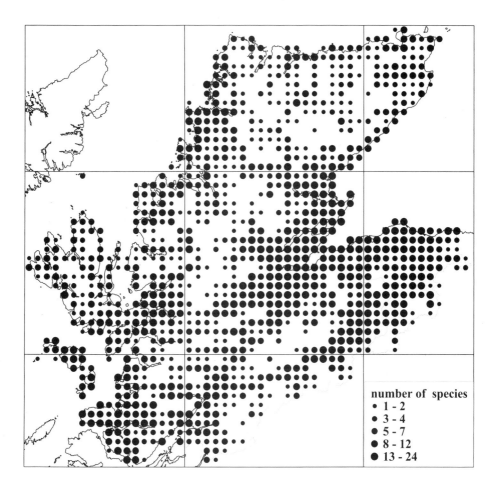

number of species
- 1 - 2
- 3 - 4
- 5 - 7
- 8 - 12
- 13 - 24

Map showing the number of species found in each 5 kilometre National Grid square during the period 1980 - 2007

CHEQUERED SKIPPER
Carterocephalus palaemon

Since its extinction in England in the 1970s, this region (with a small area of adjoining Argyll) has been the sole UK stronghold of this species. The first Butterfly Conservation reserve in Scotland, at Loch Arkaig, was established to conserve and showcase the Chequered Skipper.

Population trend. The numbers of this species, monitored on three regular transect sites in recent years, have been maintained at a satisfactory level. Repeated surveys carried out by Scottish Natural Heritage have found its core distribution to be little changed during the last twenty years, but occasional new colonies have been discovered in outlying areas.

Habitat. Woodland glades and edges, with suitable nectaring plants for the adults (bluebell and bugle are favourites). These adjoin the breeding areas, damp areas of bog-myrtle and *Molinia* grassland.

Flight period. Mid May to early July.

Larval food plant. Purple moor-grass *Molinia caerulea*.

Appearance and behaviour. This inconspicuous small butterfly, with its rapid skipping flight can be difficult to follow. When perched, its upper wing pattern of dark brown with tawny-yellow spots is displayed.

Larva feeds on the leaf blade of *Molinia*, cutting a characteristic crescent-shaped notch into its side.

Key reference: Ravenscroft (1996).

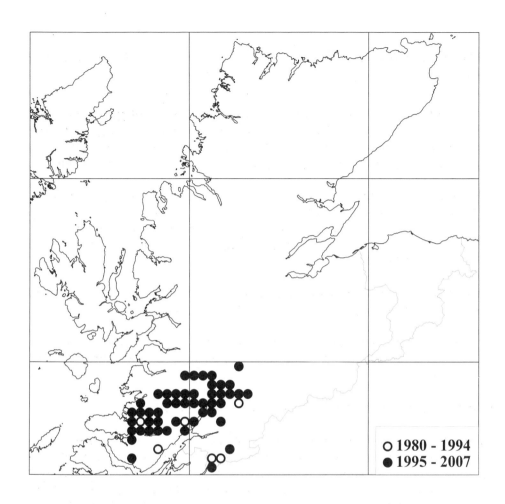

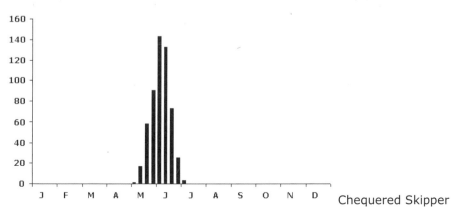

Chequered Skipper

DINGY SKIPPER
Erynnis tages

Usually favouring warm dry coastal sites in Moray and Nairn, the Dingy Skipper also occurs more locally in the Black Isle and parts of inland Inverness-shire. Our population is widely separated from the next most northerly one, which is in the far south-west of Scotland.

Population trend. In our region overall abundance has been quite stable, which contrasts with a strong decline in south Scotland and the rest of Britain. Some local colonies have been lost due to habitat change, but in other places, such as Culbin Forest, a very encouraging increase has been seen.

Habitat. Unimproved grassland sites particularly those with a sandy or gravelly character.

Flight period. Mid-May to end of June (very occasionally, a few second-brood individuals have also been seen after an unusually hot summer).

Larval food plant. Birdsfoot Trefoil *Lotus corniculatus*.

Appearance and behaviour. An inconspicuous brown moth-like butterfly, it is easily overlooked. However, it flies very actively in sunny conditions, sometimes quite late in the day, and can be seen to best advantage when feeding on flowers. In dull conditions look for it resting on heads of marram-grass, knapweed or similar flowers.

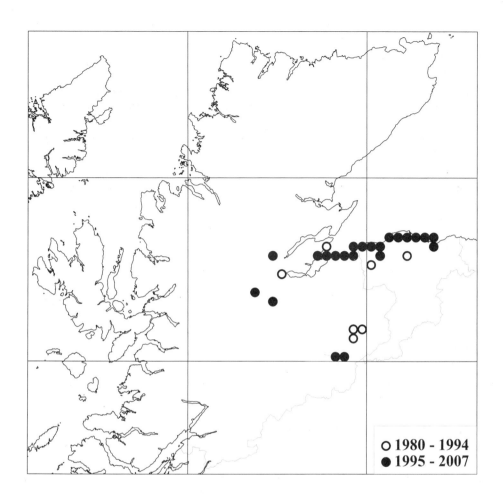

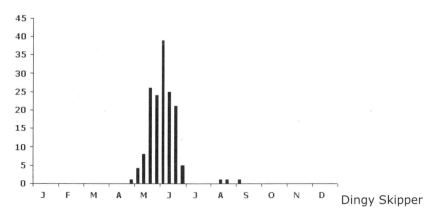

Dingy Skipper

CLOUDED YELLOW
Colias croceus

A migratory species, this now occurs fairly regularly in southern England, but very rarely and irregularly in north Scotland. The last major influx to this region was in 1992 (200+ sightings), with much smaller numbers in 2000 (26 sightings) and a few individuals in 1998 and 2006.

Population trend. Although occurrences here are unpredictable, there seems to have been a recent increase in frequency of arrivals further south.

Habitat. Very wide-ranging particularly in open country, but also sometimes visiting gardens.

Flight period. In 1992 the original influx was in May, with a second generation locally-bred appearing in August-September. In other years sightings have been on various dates between June and September.

Larval food plants. Clovers *Trifolium* species and Bird's-foot Trefoil *Lotus corniculatus*.

Appearance and behaviour. The orange-yellow and black upper wing pattern, and lemon yellow on the undersides, make this an unmistakable species when seen. A proportion of the female population has a paler, creamy-white upper wing coloration, and these individuals are distinguished as the form *helice*.

Key reference: Sutcliffe (1994).

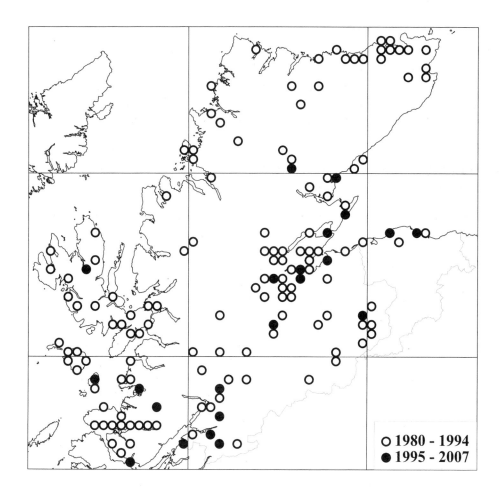

Clouded Yellow

LARGE WHITE
Pieris brassicae

This butterfly is the 'cabbage white' familiar from school biology lessons but very unwelcome in gardens as a pest of cabbages. It is widespread in the region, but with a bias towards areas of human habitation.

Population trend. Numbers fluctuate markedly from year to year, influenced by a strong input of migratory individuals in certain years.

Habitat. Wide-ranging in areas of gardens and cultivated crops, much more rarely straying into upland or uninhabited areas.

Flight period. Late May to early September.

Larval food plants. Cabbage *Brassica oleracea* and other cultivated species of the family Cruciferae.

Appearance and behaviour. Though distinctly larger than Green-veined or Small Whites, this may sometimes be confused with either of these species at a casual sighting. The differences are apparent in the photographs on Plate 3. One of the most obvious differences is in the black tip of the forewing, which extends further down the outer wing margin in this than in the Small White.

The familiar black and yellow caterpillars are very damaging to garden cabbages.

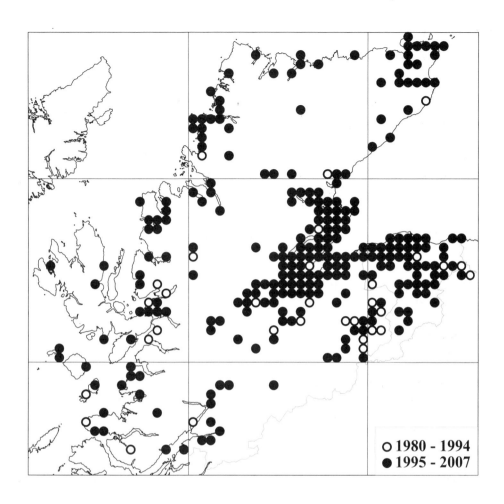

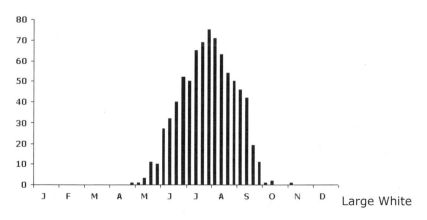

Large White

SMALL WHITE
Pieris rapae

Like the Large White this is a garden pest of cabbages. However it is usually much less common in our region, being seldom seen in the far north or in areas away from habitation.

Population trend. Highly variable from year to year, being reinforced sporadically by migration. For much of the recent recording period this butterfly appeared to have become quite scarce, but 2006 was a good year for it and so the decline may not be permanent.

Habitat. Usually quite closely restricted to gardens and cultivated crops.

Flight period. Late April to late June and again mid July to mid September.

Larval food plants. Cabbage *Brassica oleracea* and other cultivated crucifer varieties.

Appearance and behaviour. This can be distinguished from the Large White, other than by size, by the black tip on the forewing, which extends part way along the leading edge of the wing but not far down the outer edge (see Plate 3). It is possible that a proportion of our records for 'Small White' are actually misidentifications of one of the other *Pieris* species, so recorders are especially asked to look closely and make sure when identifying this butterfly.

The green caterpillar on cabbages is a little less familiar to us than the conspicuous larvae of the Large White.

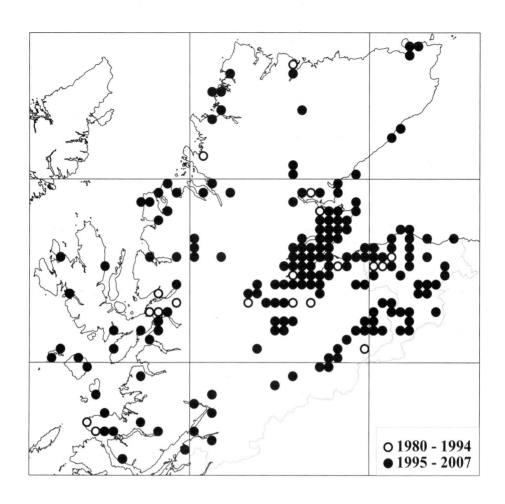

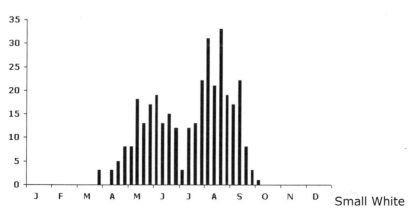

Small White

GREEN-VEINED WHITE
Pieris napi

Unquestionably this is our commonest and most widespread species; the only one currently recorded in more than half of all 5km squares in the region.

Population trend. Generally abundant every year, with only minor fluctuations in numbers and in relative size of the spring and summer generations.

Habitat. A wide variety of open habitats, but favouring damper areas such as boggy pasture and streamsides. It wanders quite widely away from breeding areas.

Flight period. Two broods in the year, the first from late April to late June, the second beginning about mid-July and continuing into early autumn. (The phenology chart does not reveal a clear gap because it combines data from different areas and different years).

Larval food plants. Cuckooflower *Cardamine pratensis,* Garlic Mustard *Alliaria petiolata* and other wild crucifers.

Appearance and behaviour. The black and white upper wing pattern is contrasted with a yellowish tone on the undersides, which additionally have a greenish-grey 'highlighting' on the veins that mark this species out from the related Large White and Small White (see Plate 3).

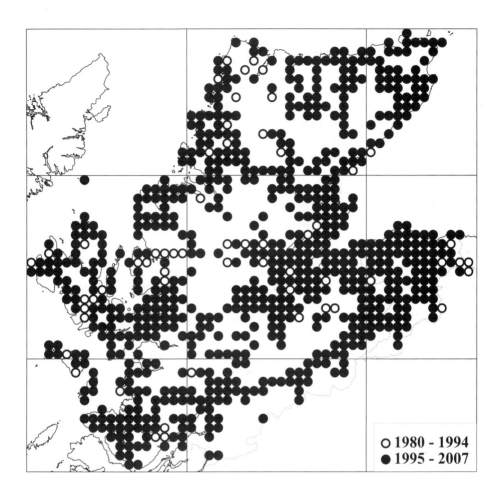

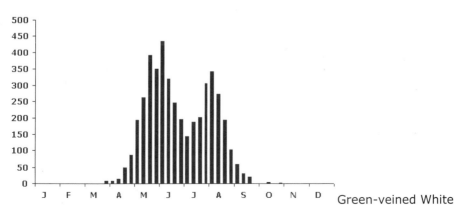

Green-veined White

ORANGE-TIP
Anthocharis cardamines

This distinctive butterfly not long ago underwent a major spread within Highland. As recently as the mid-1970s it was confined to the south-easternmost part of the region, but during the 1980s it spread rapidly both northward and westward. It colonised Skye and appeared sporadically on Rum and Eigg. On the west coast and in south-east Sutherland its distribution is probably still expanding locally at the present day. The distribution is well recorded as it was the subject of two Scotland-wide postcard surveys organised by Butterfly Conservation, in 1997-98 and again in 2007.

Population trend. In its core area the population remains strong, whereas just to the east, in lowland Aberdeenshire it seems to have declined. The long-term pattern of change is detailed here on page 6.

Habitat. Damp meadows and streamsides with an abundance of *Cardamine pratensis*.

Flight period. End of April to mid June; exceptionally to beginning of July.

Larval food plant. Cuckooflower *Cardamine pratensis*.

Appearance and behaviour. Only the male butterfly has the distinctive orange tips to the forewings. The female is essentially black-and-white but, like the male, with an attractive green mottling on the undersides. It might potentially be confused with a Green-veined White, usually on the wing at the same time (see Plate 3).

Eggs are laid singly on the flower-stalks of *Cardamine*, and these elongated bright orange eggs can be a good way to detect the presence of the species.

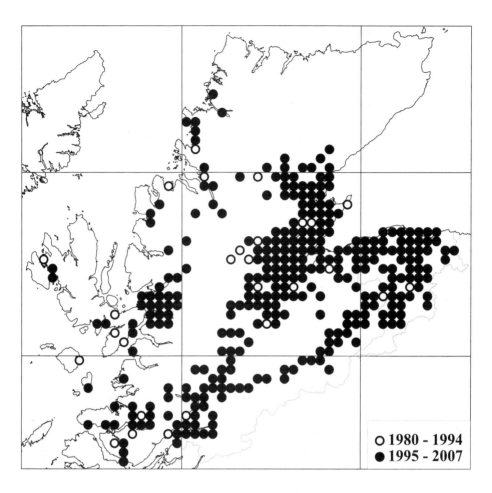

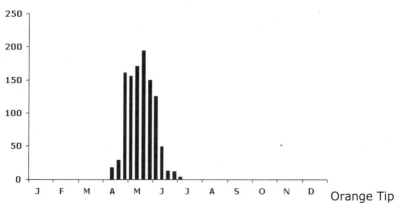

Orange Tip

GREEN HAIRSTREAK
Callophrys rubi

A widespread species particularly in the west. On the eastern side of the region it is most often seen in the central Spey valley or upland areas of Easter Ross and East Inverness. In the mid-west it occurs almost everywhere, including eastern Skye, Raasay and the Small Isles.

Population trend. The distribution seems to have been fairly stable over time, but a series of fine springs since 2000 has caused it to be more frequently recorded, particularly in the east.

Habitat. Bilberry-rich moorland and open woodland are its usual haunts, but very locally (as at Culbin Forest) it is associated more particularly with gorse scrub. In the west it extends over more general moorland habitat.

Flight period. End of April (exceptionally, earlier in April) to mid June.

Larval food plants. Bilberry *Vaccinium myrtillus*, Gorse *Ulex europaeus* and Cross-leaved Heath *Erica tetralix*.

Appearance and behaviour. A very pretty butterfly with emerald green undersides to the wings, which are the sides always displayed in perching. It is nevertheless inconspicuous because of its small size and rapid erratic flight. Often it engages in territorial combat flights involving two or more individuals.

The distinctive caterpillar, bright green with yellow transverse stripes on the back, can sometimes be found in July feeding on the flowers of Cross-leaved Heath.

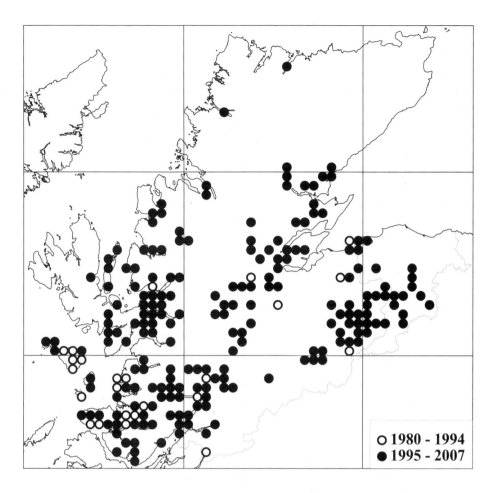

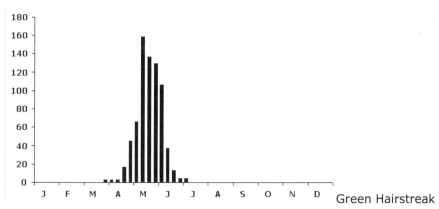

Green Hairstreak

PURPLE HAIRSTREAK
Neozephyrus quercus

This elusive butterfly has long been known to inhabit some of the oak woods of west-central Scotland as far as Argyll, but only very recently (2003 onwards) has it been seen in a limited part of our Highland region.

Population trend. It is too soon to establish any trend in numbers in the small population known to us. In other areas it seems to be subject to periodic booms, so it may be that the several sightings in 2003 and 2004 (of what is a very easily-overlooked species) reflected one of these periodic peaks in abundance.

Habitat. Mature oak woodland.

Flight period. Late July to end of August.

Larval food plants. Oaks *Quercus robur* and *Q. petraea*.

Appearance and behaviour. The spectacular purple sheen on the upper wings of the male butterfly is seldom seen in practice, as the butterflies fly mainly in the tops of oak trees, and perch with wings closed up. The underside wing pattern then revealed is a pale violet grey, with the white 'hairstreak' line running conspicuously across it. The best way to observe this species is, using binoculars, to scan the upper branches of oaks late in the day when the butterflies fly about and adopt basking positions in the evening sunshine. At other times they may descend to lower levels to feed on honeydew deposits on leaves of oak or other trees.

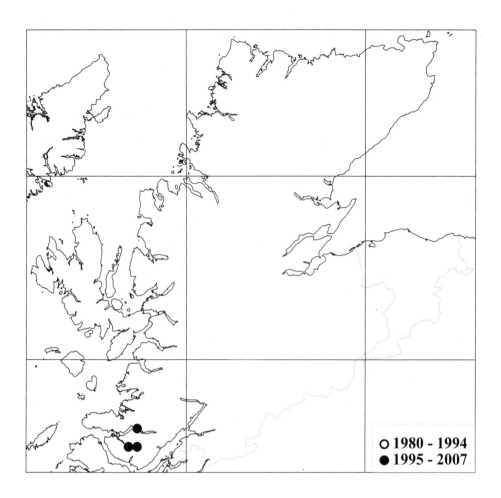

○ 1980 - 1994
● 1995 - 2007

Purple Hairstreak

SMALL COPPER
Lycaena phlaeas

A butterfly predominantly of the eastern side of our region, where it is widespread though avoiding the highest areas. Seldom is it seen in any great numbers at a time. In the west it occurs very rarely, but the few records we have suggest persisting colonies rather than vagrants.

Population trend. Maintaining its numbers well over the longer term, there are nevertheless strong fluctuations in abundance between years.

Habitat. A wide variety of open habitat types including rough grassland, farmland and coastal dunes.

Flight period. Two broods each year, from mid May to end of June and again late July to September.

Larval food plants. Sorrels *Rumex acetosa* and *R. acetosella*.

Appearance and behaviour. Seen close up this is an unmistakable butterfly. However, its flight is rapid and erratic and it can easily be lost to the eye. Not uncommonly, aberrant forms are seen such as the blue-spotted form *caeruleopunctata*.

The green slug-shaped caterpillar eats characteristic grooves in the under surface of sorrel leaves.

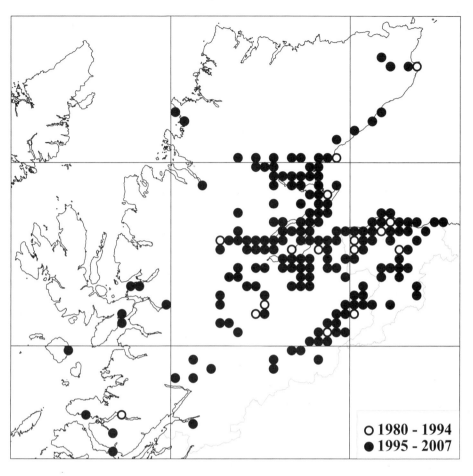

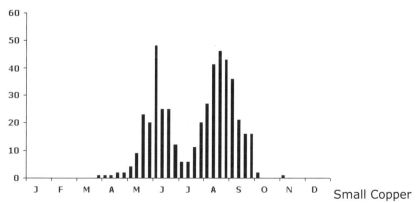

Small Copper

SMALL BLUE
Cupido minimus

The very restricted distribution of the Small Blue is linked to that of its specific larval food plant, the kidney-vetch. Although the plant is found quite widely on both sides of the region, Small Blues are confined to the eastern part.

Population trend. Populations fluctuate strongly at all sites, but most coastal colonies seem to be continuing to thrive. In east Sutherland three new colonies north of the long-known Dornoch one have been found in the last two years. However the Bettyhill colony, and some inland colonies in the south-east of the region, have not been confirmed in spite of recent searching.

Habitat. Sandy or gravelly sites with exposed bare ground which has been colonised by kidney-vetch. Mainly coastal, with a small number of inland sites typically on disused railway track or river shingles.

Flight period. Late May to early July.

Larval food plant. Kidney-vetch *Anthyllis vulneraria*.

Appearance and behaviour. An inconspicuous small butterfly which flutters close to the ground, seldom far from its food plant. The dark grey-brown upper wing colour and pale bluish undersides are distinctive (See Plate 2). In cloudy weather, or in the evening, it may be found roosting in numbers together on marram-grass etc.

Eggs and, later on, larvae may be found in the interior of the kidney-vetch flower heads in summer.

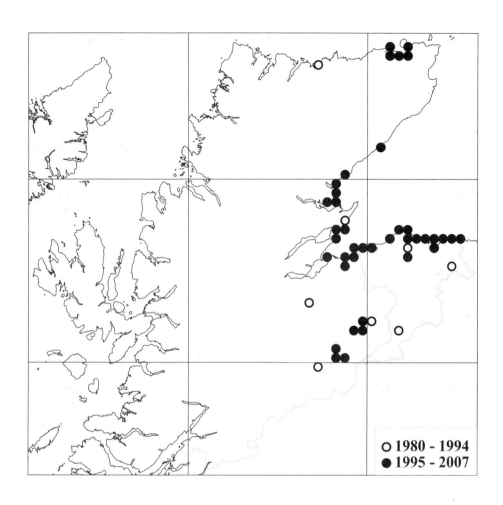

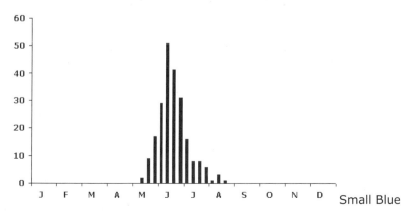

Small Blue

NORTHERN BROWN ARGUS

Priority Species

Aricia artaxerxes

Here is a species with a very restricted distribution, all of which is on the eastern side of the region. The colonies are often quite small and are localised by the occurrence of the larval food plant, rockrose. Some of the biggest colonies are in the Avon valley above and below Tomintoul.

Population trend. It is difficult to identify any definite trend given that many of our colonies have only been discovered recently. Two colonies on the Moray coast, known in the 1960s and 70s, seem to have disappeared since then.

Habitat. Base-rich grassland, often on slopes with a strong southerly exposure.

Flight period. Mid June to early August.

Larval food plant Rockrose *Helianthemum nummularium*.

Appearance and behaviour. Resembling a smaller female Common Blue, although it has blackish (not really 'brown') upper sides and a distinctive white spot in the middle of each forewing. The underside white spots, which are black-pupilled in Common Blue, are clear in this species (see Plate 2).

Eggs can readily be found on the leaves of the food plant in late summer, and the distinctive pink-striped green larva can be found on rockrose foliage from autumn through until late spring.

Key reference: Franco *et al* (2006).

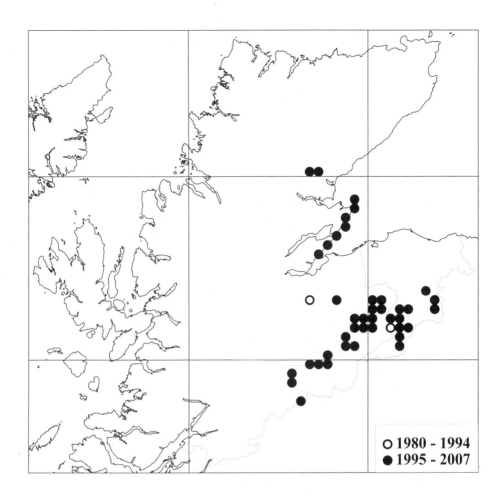

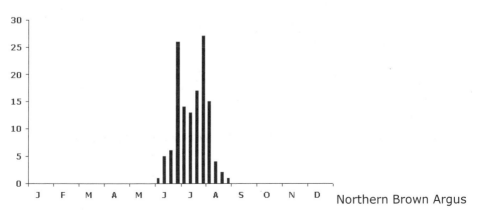

Northern Brown Argus

Plate1 :- a and b - Pearl-bordered Fritillary.
c and d - Small Pearl-bordered Fritillary
e and f - Dark Green Fritillary

Plate 2 : a - Common Blue, pair mating
b - Common Blue, male
c - Common Blue, female
d and e – Northern Brown Argus
f and g – Small Blue

Identifying Pearl-bordered and Small Pearl-bordered Fritillary

The safest way to distinguish Pearl-bordered from Small Pearl-bordered
Fritillary is by looking at the underside of the hind wings. The Pearl-bordered
has only two silvery marks on the inner part of the wing while the Small
Pearl-bordered has seven – see photos.

With a good view or, better still, a photograph it is often possible to tell them
apart from the upper wing as shown below (from photographs of live
butterflies).

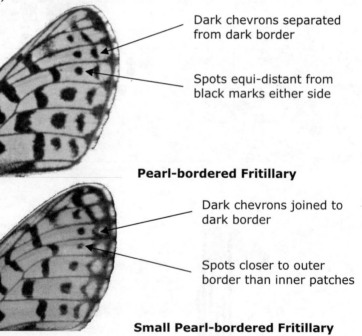

Dark chevrons separated
from dark border

Spots equi-distant from
black marks either side

Pearl-bordered Fritillary

Dark chevrons joined to
dark border

Spots closer to outer
border than inner patches

Small Pearl-bordered Fritillary

Plate 1

Plate 2

Plate 3

Plate 4

Plate 3 :   a and b – Large White
c and d – Small White
e and f – Green-veined White
g and h – Orange-tip

Plate 4 :   a - Small Heath
b - Large Heath
c – Meadow Brown
d - Ringlet
e – Scotch Argus
f – Mountain Ringlet
g – Speckled Wood
h - Grayling

Identifying Large, Small and Green-veined Whites

Great care often has to be taken in separating these three species. The Green-veined White is the commonest of the three in our area, but it can be very variable. The photographs here cannot show the full range of variation, so check out the identification guides for more details.

The Large White has more extensive black on the wing tip than the other two, while the underside of the hind wing on the Green-veined White shows the green veins that give it its name.

Identifying Small and Large Heath

Large Heaths in northern Scotland are much plainer than specimens from the south. They have only small and faint eyespots (particularly on the hindwing) and so can look quite similar to Small Heath.

Both species rest with wings folded up over the back, so generally the underside features have to be used for identification. Three key differences are found in these:

- the eyespot on the forewing is within the pale streak in Small Heath, slightly beyond the pale streak in Large Heath;
- the pale patch near the middle of the hindwing is rounded in Small Heath but drawn out to a point in Large Heath;
- there is a sharp contrast between dark inner and pale outer areas of the hindwing in Small Heath, but a more gradual change in shading in Large Heath.

COMMON BLUE
Polyommatus icarus

A familiar and attractive butterfly of high summer, this species is very widely distributed, but seldom seen in very large numbers in one place.

Population trend. Although remaining widespread, it seems that, particularly in the East Inverness and Moray part of the region, the Common Blue is less abundant now than at the start of our recording period.

Habitat. Grassy sites, from sea level to high in the mountains, where Bird's-foot Trefoil is established.

Flight period. Mid June to late August. Some fresh specimens appearing in September or October may represent an occasional second generation.

Larval food plant. Bird's-foot Trefoil *Lotus corniculatus*.

Appearance and behaviour. A bright metallic sky-blue coloration denotes the male of this species, whilst the female is a darker brown-suffused violet blue, with a series of orange lunules towards the edge of each wing (see Plate 2). Outside its activity period in the day, it may be found roosting in small numbers together on grass-stems or shrubs.

The shining white egg is easily found on Bird's-foot Trefoil leaves in summer.

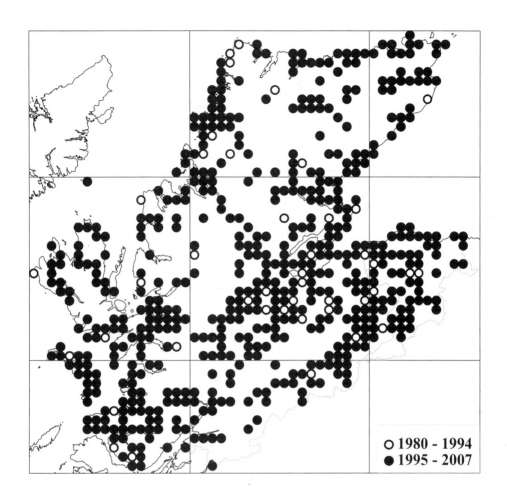

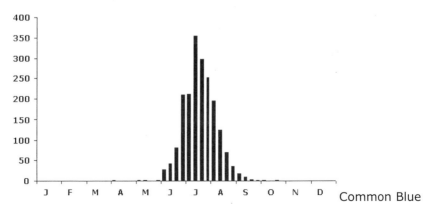

Common Blue

RED ADMIRAL
Vanessa atalanta

This familiar butterfly is a migrant to the UK, but until recently was not believed to survive the British winter. Recent observations have proved that it can hibernate successfully, and it has probably done so in the last 3-4 years, even in Highland.

Population trend. Variable from year to year, but generally much commoner here now than it was twenty years ago or so.

Habitat. Widespread both in open country and woodland habitats. A frequent visitor to gardens to feed on Buddleia or other flowers or on rotting fruit.

Flight period. Most often arriving as a migrant in late May or June, then breeding to produce offspring which fly from late summer well into the autumn. Some may be able to survive a mild winter by hibernating, which explains why recently one or two have been seen on fine days in January or February.

Larval food plant. Common nettle *Urtica dioica*.

Appearance and behaviour. Its striking black-and-white red-banded pattern makes the Red Admiral one of our most iconic butterflies. It is often our latest-flying species in October or even November.

The larvae are to be seen on nettles in summer, feeding singly in spun-together leaves unlike those of Peacock or Small Tortoiseshell.

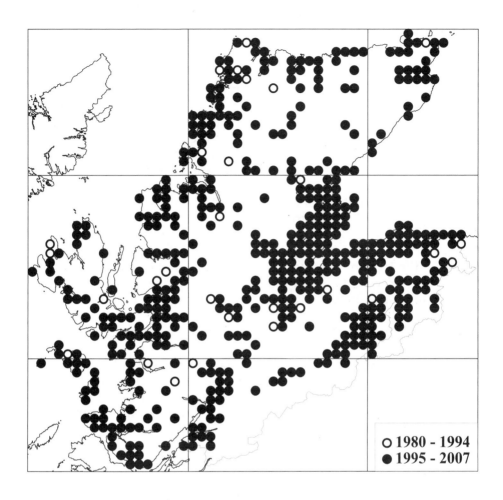

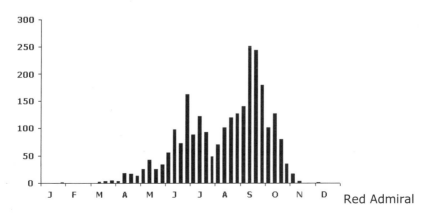

Red Admiral

PAINTED LADY
Cynthia cardui

This migratory species is now seen with us in most years.

Population trend. Numbers highly variable from year to year: 1996 and 2003 were particularly good years in the recent period. Overall, however, it is now much more abundant and more frequently observed than even 13 years ago at the start of the recording period.

Habitat. Widespread in open country, often favouring gardens and flower-rich areas of waste ground.

Flight period. The phenology chart shows an irregular pattern reflecting the different timing of immigration in different years. A normal pattern would be of a main migratory influx in June, and a second generation locally-bred appearing in the autumn.

Larval food plants. Thistles *Cirsium vulgare* and *C. palustre*.

Appearance and behaviour. A distinctive large butterfly with salmon-pink upper side and elaborately patterned underside markings. It is, like the other Vanessid species, sometimes seen at high altitudes on mountains, in the phenomenon known as 'hill-topping' which seems to be a feature of the migration or dispersal behaviour.

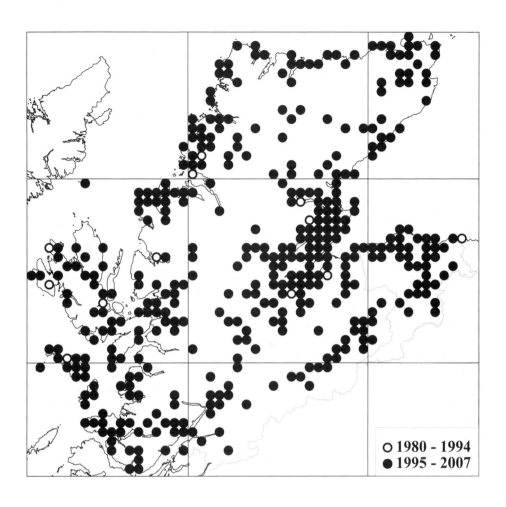

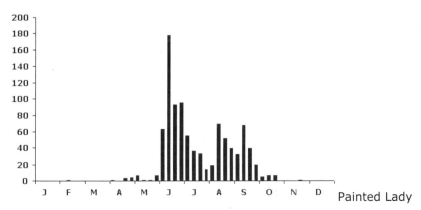

Painted Lady

43

SMALL TORTOISESHELL
Aglais urticae

Vying with the Meadow Brown to be our second most widespread species, the Small Tortoiseshell is slightly less well-represented in the western and central parts of the region than it is in the east.

Population trend. The population fluctuations of this species have been quite large, but in the last 3-4 years numbers here have been well down on previous levels.

Habitat. Very widespread, but, breeding on nettles, it is commonest in areas with some 'enrichment' due to human activity.

Flight period. After hibernation, flying from April to June, the next brood appearing from late July through to September.

Larval food plant. Common nettle *Urtica dioica*.

Appearance and behaviour. This handsome tawny-red butterfly with thin blue-lined margins to the wings is familiar to all. It is probably still our commonest garden butterfly, particularly noticeable in the autumn when feeding on Buddleia etc. Adults frequently enter houses and other buildings, from quite early in the autumn, to hibernate.

The larvae feed colonially on nettles in summer.

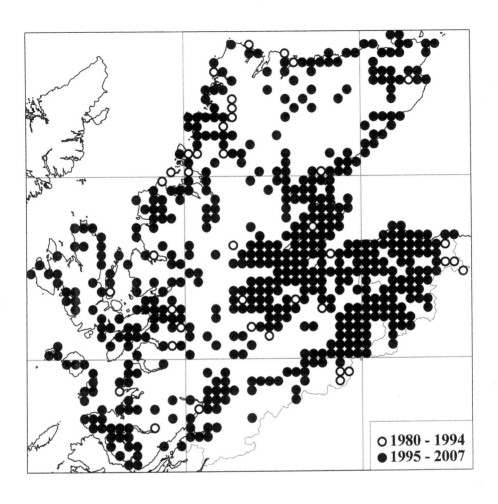

O 1980 - 1994
● 1995 - 2007

Correction –   The Red Admiral map was repeated as Small Tortoiseshell.
This is the correct Small Tortoiseshell map.

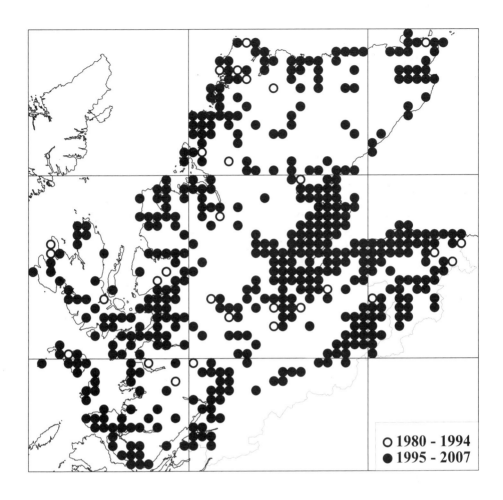

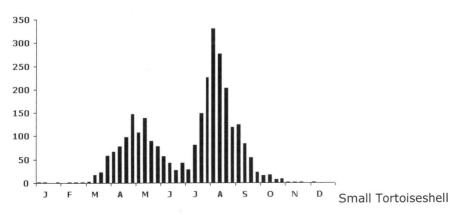

Small Tortoiseshell

PEACOCK
Inachis io

Until the year 2002 this butterfly was no more than a vagrant to this region, appearing as scattered single individuals at irregular intervals. In September 2002 there was a sudden huge influx (presumably migratory, but the origins of the flight are uncertain) to the whole of eastern Inverness-shire and Moray. Since then the Peacock has been a permanent resident and has extended its distribution into the rest of the region. For more details of this range expansion, see page 8.

Population trend. Since 2002 numbers have been good each year in the original influx area. A further major increase and spread occurred in 2006, since when it has been seen right up to the north coast and across into Skye and the islands.

Habitat. A wide range of habitat types is used for breeding, otherwise also on mountains where it sometimes seems to migrate in large numbers.

Flight period. End of March to early June, then again early August through to October (after which it enters hibernation). Increasingly too we are seeing occasional individuals emerging briefly in fine weather during the winter months.

Larval food plant. Common nettle *Urtica dioica*.

Appearance and behaviour. This butterfly with its prominent eyespots on the wings is recognisable even to non-naturalists. Hibernation behaviour has been confirmed here by the finding of butterflies in wood-stacks, sheds and occasionally in houses.

In spring often to be seen feeding on sallow catkins in the wider countryside, in autumn more often seen in gardens.

The black spiny caterpillars occur on nettles in mid-summer.

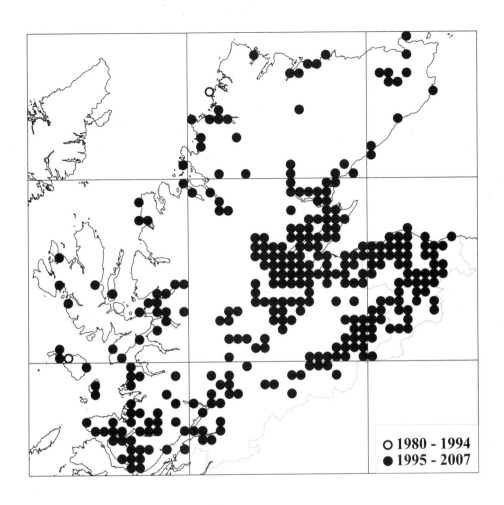

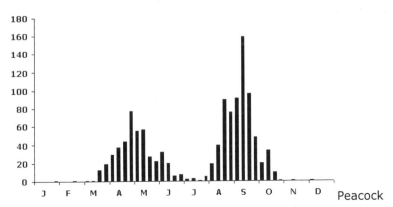

Peacock

CAMBERWELL BEAUTY
Nymphalis antiopa

This is a large handsome butterfly which appears only as a very occasional migrant here. The map shows that it arrives most often on the east side of the region, being a migrant from continental Europe. During the present recording period there were 27 reported seen here, the best years being 1995 (four) 1996 (five) 2006 (nine) and 2007 (six).

Population trend. The appearances of this species are so irregular that it is difficult to detect a definite trend, but it does seem to have had more reported sightings here in the last 13 years than was usual in earlier years.

Habitat. Like our common Vanessid species, this butterfly seems to range widely through the countryside, sometimes visiting gardens to feed at flowers or rotting fruit.

Flight period. Immigrations occur in the autumn months. Sometimes overwintered individuals then re-emerge in April and May (several instances in the spring of 2007).

Larval food plants. No breeding has ever been proved in the UK, but on the continent larvae are found on sallow, poplar and other trees.

Appearance and behaviour. This is an unmistakable butterfly due to its large size and dark purple-brown wings with broad cream-coloured borders. Has been sighted in spring, after emergence from hibernation, when feeding on sallow catkins.

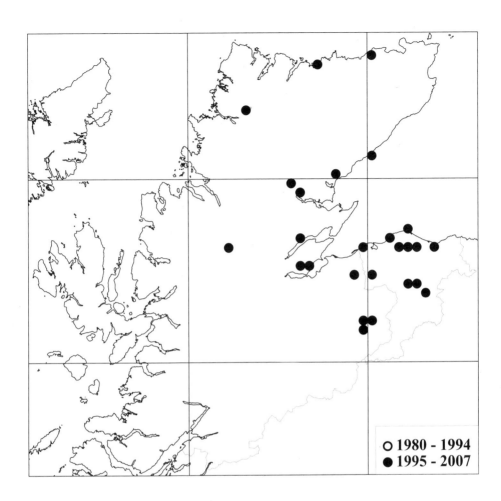

Legend:

○ 1980 - 1994
● 1995 - 2007

Camberwell Beauty

SMALL PEARL-BORDERED FRITILLARY
Boloria selene   **Priority Species**

This attractive butterfly, now severely threatened in parts of southern Britain, is widespread and locally abundant over a large part of our area. The apparent density of the distribution map does not mean it occurs everywhere, however, as it is colonial and confined to particular habitat types.

Population trend. There is little sign of any decrease in this species' abundance here, in marked contrast to its relative the Pearl-bordered Fritillary. On the contrary it seems to be increasing in some places, as for example at the long-term transect site at Insh Marshes.

Habitat. Mainly in damp grassland areas, quite extensively in the west but more locally in the east.

Flight period. End of May to late July (sometimes just into August).

Larval food plant. Marsh violet *Viola palustris*.

Appearance and behaviour. The similarity to Pearl-bordered Fritillary can cause confusion, particularly as the two can occur together on the same site and, despite the name, size is no guide to distinguishing them. The Small Pearl-bordered Fritillary has a later flight period than the Pearl-bordered, starting 2-3 weeks later on average, so when the two are flying together the Pearl-bordered often already has a worn or faded appearance. For more reliable diagnostic features see Plate 1 and page 36.

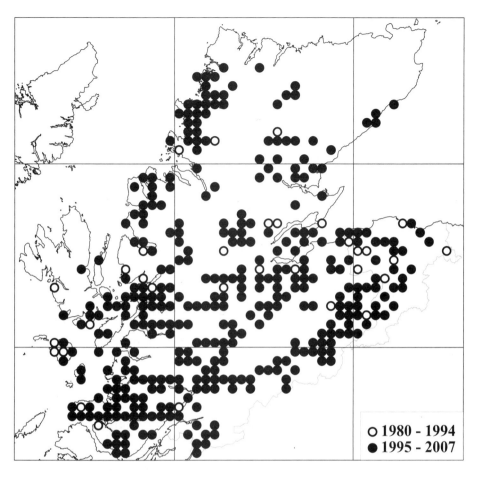

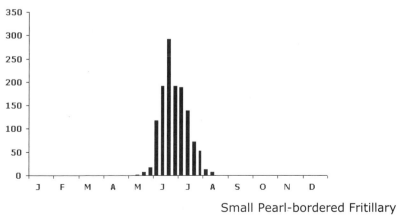

Small Pearl-bordered Fritillary

PEARL-BORDERED FRITILLARY

Boloria euphrosyne

Regarded as a nationally threatened species, the Pearl-bordered Fritillary is locally distributed over quite a large part of our region. It is much less common and widespread than the Small Pearl-bordered Fritillary, being absent from most of the coastal districts, from the far north and from all of the islands. The map shows it has lost a high proportion of sites since 1980-94 in the east of the region.

Population trend. Evidently declining: an intensive national survey in 1997-98 found or confirmed many sites in the Highlands, and this may have masked to some extent the real state of decline. Certainly in 2000-07 the number of confirmed sites has been lower.

Habitat. Open areas in woodlands, especially where there is a base-rich soil and abundance of violets – bracken is nearly always present too. Sometimes also sheltered areas on moorland.

Flight period. Early May to mid-June (later in high-altitude sites in the Cairngorms).

Larval food plant. Dog violet *Viola riviniana*.

Appearance and behaviour. This species is very difficult to distinguish in flight from the Small Pearl-bordered Fritillary and, being fast-flying and difficult to approach, it can best be identified by capturing and examining close up. The distinguishing features of the two species are shown in Plate 1 and on page 36.

The caterpillar can sometimes be found basking on dead fronds of bracken in the spring.

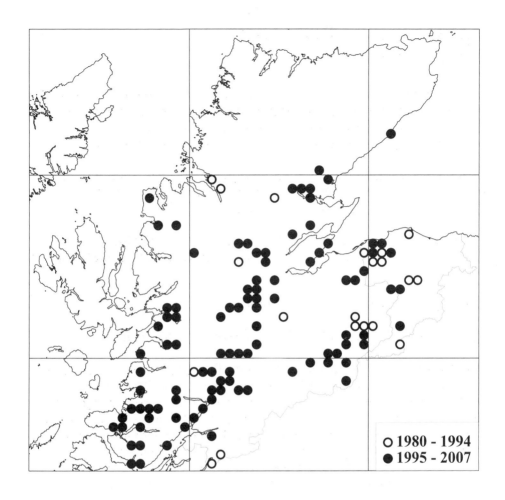

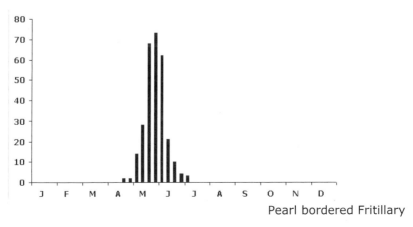

Pearl bordered Fritillary

DARK GREEN FRITILLARY
Argynnis aglaja

Our largest fritillary, it is widespread across the whole region including the islands. It is nevertheless quite localised in its occurrence, and is absent from agricultural lowland areas in the east. Occasional wanderers appear quite far from the breeding areas however.

Population trend. Though fluctuating year-to-year, numbers have held up well over the long term. There is some indication of an increase in the eastern part of the region.

Habitat. A wide range of grassland and moorland habitats in the west: on the east it is more strictly confined to either coastal areas or upland glens.

Flight period. Late June to end of August.

Larval food plants. Violets *Viola riviniana* and *V. palustris*.

Appearance and behaviour. A strong flier which can be difficult to approach, unless settled to feed on a flower head. Its name is a misnomer as the prevailing wing-colour is a rich tawny orange, the green shading being restricted to the underside hind wings (see Plate 1). Our populations include some very distinctively-marked dark individuals, particularly striking in female specimens, which are distinguished as the form *scotica*. This comprises quite a high proportion of the population in some western and island sites.

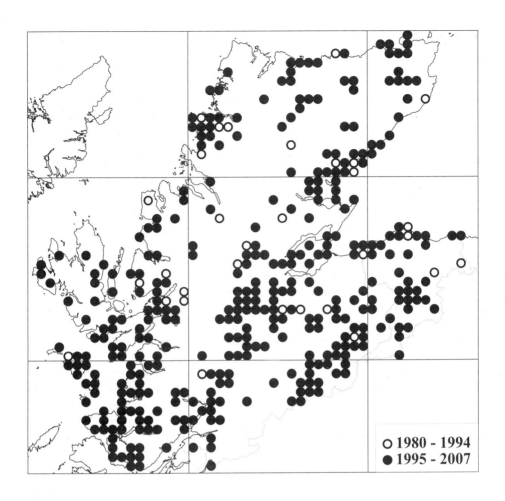

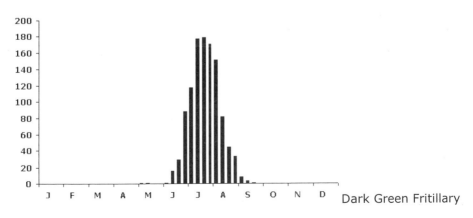

Dark Green Fritillary

MARSH FRITILLARY
Euphydryas aurinia

A species found here on the very edge of its range, the main stronghold in Scotland being in coastal Argyll and the islands to the south-west of our region. Nationally it is a species in severe decline.

Population trend. Insufficient information to identify a trend, since over many years there have been only sporadic records. (The few records in south-west Highland in the 1970s or early 80s seem to be poorly documented.) In its main distribution area, the populations fluctuate cyclically with peaks about every 6 years.

Habitat. Damp unimproved grassland (including lightly-grazed pasture) with a good growth of devil's-bit scabious.

Flight period. End of May to early July.

Larval food plant. Devil's-bit scabious *Succisa pratensis*.

Appearance and behaviour. A strongly-flying butterfly, it often co-occurs, in time and place, with the Small Pearl-bordered Fritillary. At a distance it may be distinguished from this by its less tawny appearance and more direct flight. Seen close up it is a handsome butterfly with bands of orange-red alternating with pale straw and dark brown colours.

Its larvae feed colonially and make large webs on the foliage of scabious, which they occupy throughout the autumn and again in the spring.

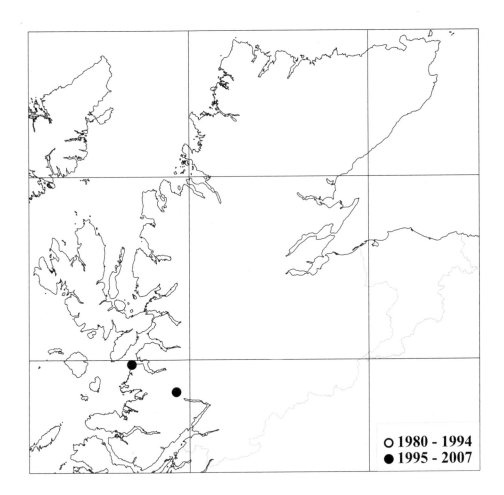

O 1980 - 1994
● 1995 - 2007

Marsh Fritillary

SPECKLED WOOD
Pararge aegeria

Our most shade-tolerant butterfly, it is associated with woodland habitats including quite dense conifer plantation. It has expanded its distribution hugely in the region, over a period of 40 years or more during which it colonised all of its present eastern range and spread significantly northwards on the west side (see Page 7).

Population trend. The increase and spread of the Speckled Wood has been very long-continued, with its fastest development probably in the 1970s, when it colonised most of Moray, and in the early 1990s when it spread through Easter Ross into Sutherland. Since 2000 it has also colonised limited areas in Caithness and north-central Sutherland.

Habitat. Both conifer and broadleaved woodland, also areas of well-developed scrub and mature gardens.

Flight period. Late April to June and again in July to early October. The latter period may include two separate broods, as there is usually a clear fall-off in numbers between late summer and autumn (not apparent in the phenology chart, which combines data from many different years).

Larval food plants. Grasses including False Brome *Brachypodium sylvaticum*, Couch grass *Elymus repens* and Cock's-foot *Dactylis glomerata*.

Appearance and behaviour. This brown butterfly with cream-yellow speckling is completely distinctive when seen. Its behaviour, fluttering along woodland tracks and stopping occasionally to bask in patches of sunlight, is also characteristic. Males defend small territories and engage in tumbling 'challenge' flights with intruders.

Key references: Barbour (1986), McAllister (1993).

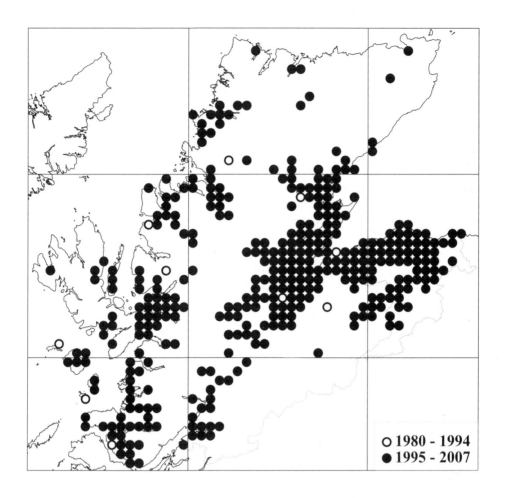

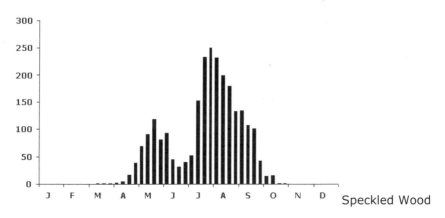

Speckled Wood

MOUNTAIN RINGLET
Erebia epiphron

This is the UK's only truly montane butterfly species, confined to the Highlands of Scotland and the Cumbrian mountains in England. In our region it occurs mainly in the southern Monadhliaths, the Ben Nevis and Mamores ranges and the Glencoe area.

Population trend. Due to the remoteness of its habitats and scarcity of good weather conditions in which to record, this is a difficult species to monitor. A single transect site in the region, at Creag Meagaidh, has recorded Mountain Ringlet since 2003, and numbers have fluctuated widely. It has been predicted that this species will suffer as a result of climate warming. A survey in 2004-5 by scientists from York University concluded that populations had retreated by 150 metres in elevation (uphill) over a 20-year period.

Habitat. Montane grassland, between about 300 and 1000m elevation, generally on base-rich ground and usually with a southerly exposure.

Flight period. Late June to early August.

Larval food plant. Mat grass *Nardus stricta*.

Appearance and behaviour. This butterfly resembles a smaller, duller version of its relative the Scotch Argus (see Plate 4). It flies rather strongly in good sunshine, but in overcast cooler conditions, more frequent in its mountain habitat, it settles in the vegetation and is then difficult to find.

Key references: McGowan (1997), Franco *et al* (2006).

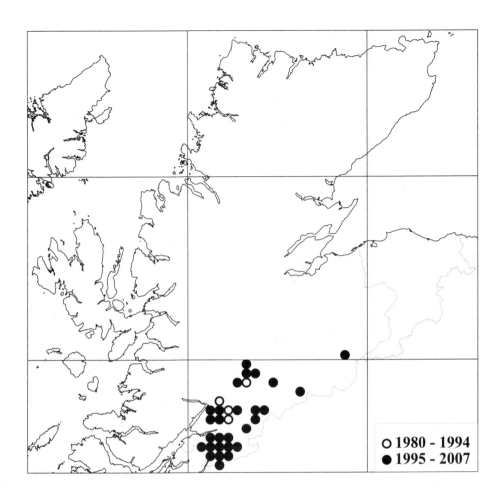

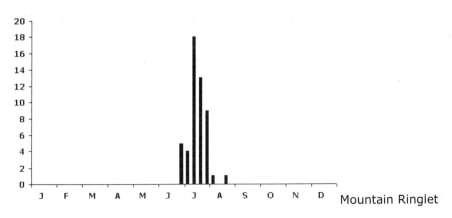

Mountain Ringlet

SCOTCH ARGUS
Erebia aethiops

Numerically one of our commonest species, the Scotch Argus is widespread over a large part of the mainland being absent only from most of east Sutherland and Caithness. It is absent also from the Small Isles and fairly sparsely distributed in west Sutherland and north-west Ross. Although it is one of the UK's few distinctively northern butterflies, it is not especially upland in its occurrence, being found from sea-level to about 500m and wandering occasionally to higher levels in hot weather.

Population trend. Population size and distribution have both been very stable over the recent period. A single sighting in Caithness (2004) may represent a new colonization, and there is some indication of increasing frequency in west Sutherland.

Habitat. A wide range of grassland habitats is favoured, particularly sheltered areas such as woodland rides and clearings, woodland edges and open scrub sites. More open situations such as coastal slopes and upland rough pasture are also occupied.

Flight period. Late July - early September.

Larval food plant. Purple moor-grass *Molinia caerulea*.

Appearance and behaviour. This distinctive dark chocolate-brown butterfly has white-pupilled black spots in an orange-red band towards the outer edge of each wing (see Plate 4). Its flight is rather leisurely and this is one of our more easily approachable butterflies.

Key references: Waddell, Neath & Kirkland (2005), Franco *et al* (2006).

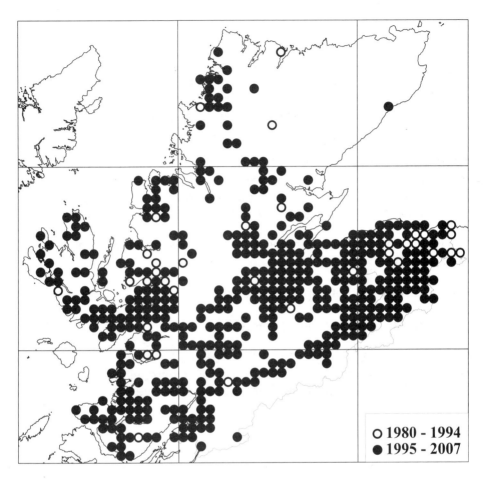

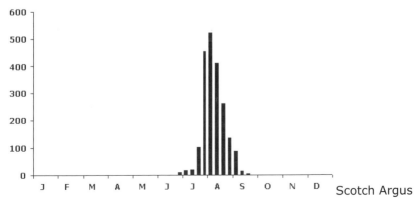

Scotch Argus

GRAYLING
Hipparchia semele

As in most of Scotland, this is strictly a coastal species in our area. The Grayling now occurs all round our coast except for a gap of approximately 100 miles between Cape Wrath in the west and Golspie in the east. Before 1980 however there were a very few isolated sightings along the north coast of Sutherland and Caithness.

Population trend. A general decline has been evident since the 1970s, particularly in parts of the west. Some losses seem to have occurred even before the start of our recording period, and a more recent down-turn seems possibly to have been underway since 2000.

Habitat. Coastal cliffs, shingles and dunes (exceptionally on rocky slopes up to 2-3 miles inland).

Flight period. End of June – end of August.

Larval food plants. Various grasses.

Appearance and behaviour. The mottled brown and grey underwing pattern disguises the Grayling very well as it perches with wings closed against a rock surface. But it is a very active flier in courtship and 'territorial' challenges and is then more often seen.

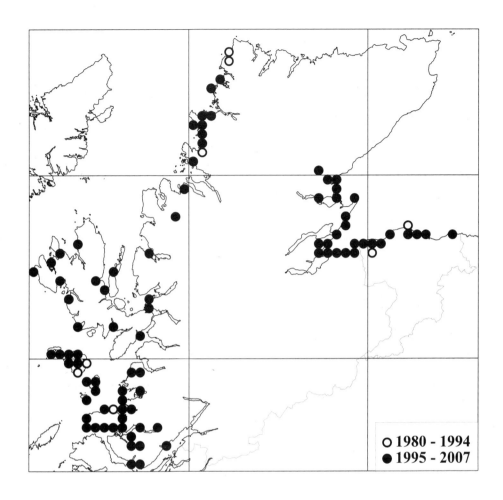

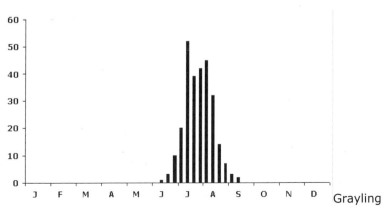

Grayling

MEADOW BROWN
Maniola jurtina

Although evidently our second most widespread butterfly species, the Meadow Brown is not entirely ubiquitous in the region. It is sparsely distributed or even absent from some central and upland areas, such as parts of Lochaber, mid-Ross and central Sutherland.

Population trend. Maintaining its numbers in the long term, but subject to shorter-term fluctuations of a cyclical nature.

Habitat. A variety of open grassland habitats including coastal dunes, woodland clearings, and rough pasture.

Flight period. Late June to mid August.

Larval food plants. Various grasses.

Appearance and behaviour. This large brown butterfly has tawny-orange patches on the upper wing, paler and more extensive in the female. A single eyespot in the apex of each forewing distinguishes it from the Scotch Argus which has several eyespots (see Plate 4).

The males in particular are quite strong fliers.

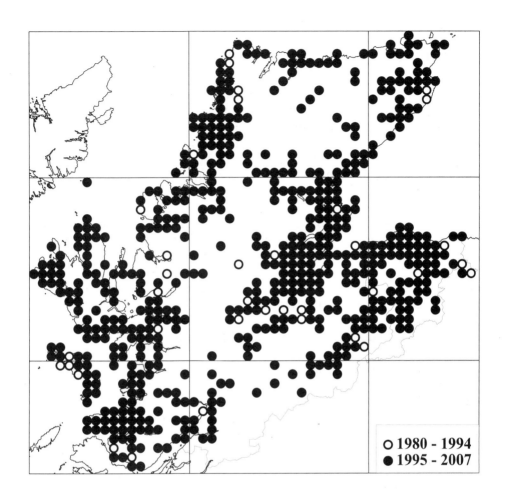

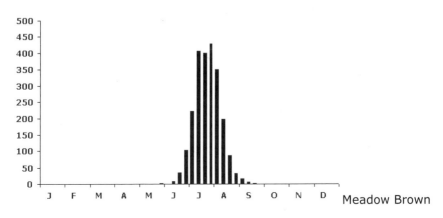

Meadow Brown

RINGLET
Aphantopus hyperantus

Until very recently this butterfly's northern range limit was in Aberdeenshire just outside our region. Perhaps in response to climate change, it has moved rapidly to colonise Moray and Speyside and to found colonies beyond that even as far as south-east Sutherland. On the west side too there have been scattered sightings, but as yet less definite evidence of colonization (see 'Expanding Species in Highland and Moray).

Population trend. The build-up of population has been so rapid that the Ringlet has increased from nothing to become almost a common species (in Speyside and Strathavon) in just 4 or 5 years.

Habitat. Damp grassland, usually of rank growth and with some shelter provided by scrub or woodland edge.

Flight period. Late June to beginning of August.

Larval food plants. Various grasses.

Appearance and behaviour. Seen at a distance this is a drab grey-brown butterfly which might be mistaken for a slightly under-sized Meadow Brown. Close up, the 'ringlets' of golden yellow lining the undersides of the wings make it unmistakable (see Plate 4). Fresh specimens also have a very distinct white fringe on the outer wing edges.

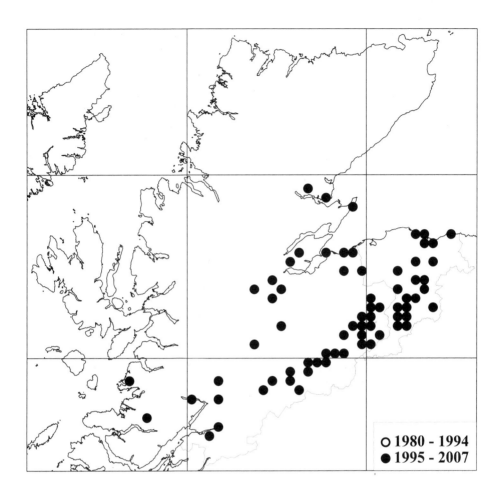

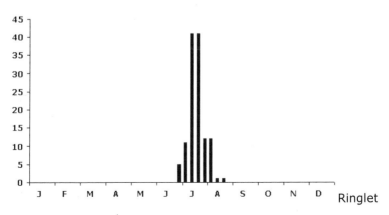

Ringlet

SMALL HEATH
Coenonympha pamphilus

A very widespread species of grassland habitats in which it ranges from sea level to at least 500m up in the mountains. It occurs on all the larger islands, but is absent from parts of the far north.

Population trend. Numbers have continued quite strong in the west, but in eastern areas there seems to have been something of a decline. In Moray the species has disappeared from agricultural lowlands, and is now confined either to the coast or upland areas.

Habitat. A variety of grassland types including coastal dunes, rough pasture, woodland clearings and moorland edges.

Flight period. End of May to early August.

Larval food plants. Various grasses, particularly fescues, *Festuca* species.

Appearance and behaviour. This is a small but easily-observed butterfly which flies close to the ground and perches frequently with wings closed up. The underside pattern then revealed allows this species to be distinguished from the Large Heath (see Plate 4).

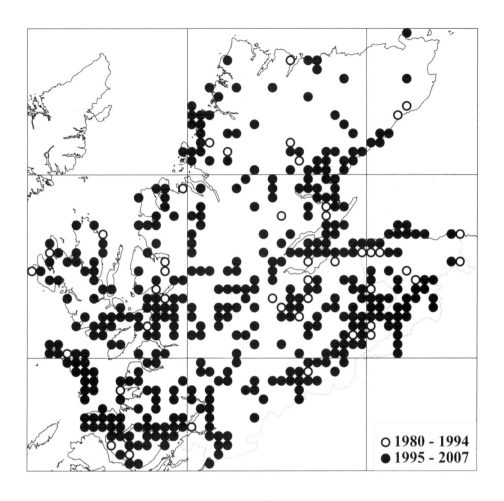

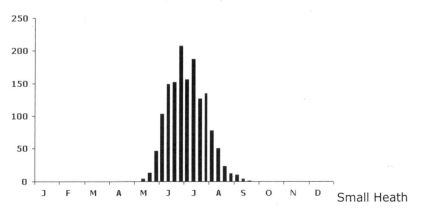

Small Heath

LARGE HEATH
Coenonympha tullia

This region contains the largest concentration of this northerly species in the UK. It occurs very widely in acid boggy habitats, including on the larger islands, but has its strongest populations on the peatlands of Sutherland and Caithness.

Population trend. This is one of the species forecast to suffer losses as a result of climate change (on the basis that warmer climate will reduce the suitability of its habitat). Certainly the evidence suggests it is already starting to decline here: although still strong in the far north, there is a shortage of recent records in other parts of Highland (eg Wester Ross), and also particularly in Moray.

Habitat. Boggy moorland, including lowland raised bogs and also ascending to at least 600m in the mountains.

Flight period. Mid June to early August.

Larval food plant. Hare's-tail cotton-grass *Eriophorum vaginatum*.

Appearance and behaviour. This butterfly is a powerful flier which can be difficult to approach. It can be distinguished from the Small Heath by its greyer appearance and different pattern of light banding on the underside hind wing (see Plate 4). It is of course also larger, but occasional smaller individuals may approach the Small Heath in size. Our local form is the subspecies *scotica*, which lacks the large eyespots characteristic of more southern subspecies.

Key reference: Franco, *et al* (2006).

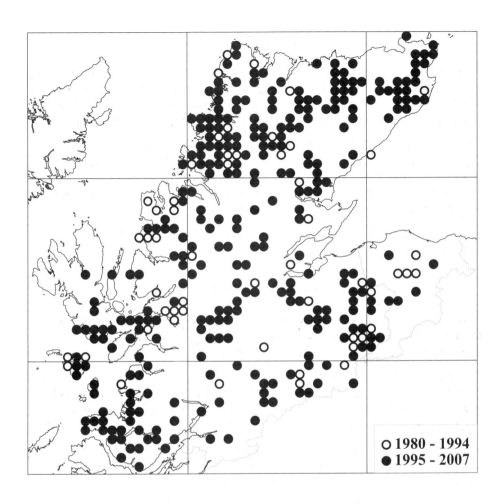

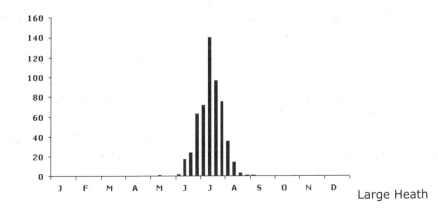

Large Heath

Occasional visitors

The above 30 species accounts deal with all resident butterfly species and regularly occurring migrants that have been observed here since 1980. There are also a few species which have turned up once or twice as scarce migrants (or perhaps accidental introductions).

The Comma *Polygonia c-album* has recently appeared twice in the region, at Fort Augustus (2004) and Abernethy (2006). Single sightings have been reported of Short-tailed Blue *Cupido argiades*, a very scarce migrant to the UK, and of the Small Skipper *Thymelicus sylvestris* and Swallowtail *Papilio machaon*.

Older records of vagrant and scarce migrant species were detailed in *The Butterflies of Scotland* (Thomson 1980).

Text references

Barbour, D.A. (1986) **Expansion of the range of the Speckled Wood butterfly, *Pararge aegeria* (Linn.), in north-east Scotland.** *Entomologist's Record*, **98**, 98-105.

Franco, A.M.A., Hill, J.K., Kitschke, C., Collingham, Y.C., Roy, D.B., Fox, R., Huntley, B. and Thomas, C.D. (2006) **Impacts of climate warming and habitat loss on extinctions at species' low-latitude range boundaries**. *Global Change Biology* **12**, 1545-1553.

McAllister, D.W. (1993) **The spread of the Speckled Wood butterfly, *Pararge aegeria* (Linn.) in Easter Ross and Sutherland**. *Butterfly Conservation News* **53**, 44-48.

McGowan, G. (1997) **The distribution of the Small Mountain Ringlet, *Erebia epiphron mnemon* (Haworth, 1812) in Scotland**. *Entomologist's Gazette* **48**, 135-145.

Ravenscroft, N.O.M. (1996) **The Chequered Skipper**. Butterfly Conservation.

Sutcliffe, R. (1994) **The Clouded Yellow invasion of Scotland**, 1992. *Glasgow Naturalist*, **22(4)**, 389-396.

Waddell, J., Neath, B. and Kirkland, P. (2005) **Recent high altitude observations of Scotch Argus *Erebia aethiops* (Esp.) in Scotland**. *Atropos* **26**, 20-22.

Further reading

Pocket Guide to the Butterflies of Great Britain and Ireland
Richard Lewington. British Wildlife Publishing (2003).
The best identification guide to British and Irish butterflies.

The Butterflies of Scotland – a natural history
George Thomson. Croom Helm (1980).
A comprehensive historical account of butterflies in Scotland up to 1980.

Millennium Atlas of Butterflies in Britain and Ireland
Jim Asher, Martin Warren, Richard Fox, Paul Harding, Gail Jeffcoate and Stephen Jeffcoate. Oxford (2001).
The results of a nationwide survey from 1995 to 1999 with reference to records from earlier years. Detailed information is given on populations, phenology, conservation and trends.

The State of Butterflies in Britain and Ireland
Richard Fox, Jim Asher, Tom Brereton, David Roy and Martin Warren. Pisces Publications (2006).
An update of the Millennium Atlas covering 2000 – 2004.

Butterflies of the Highlands - Dealain-dè na Gàidhealtachd
A handy free identification guide with notes and photographs of the Highland species, where to see them and how to record them, published by Butterfly Conservation Scotland.

Butterflies of South West Scotland. An Atlas of their Distribution
Keith Futter, Richard Sutcliffe, David Welham, Anne Welham, A. John Rostron, Jessie MacKay, Neil Gregory, Jim McCleary, T. Norman Tait, Jim Black and Paul Kirkland. Argyll Publishing (2006).

Butterfly Atlas of the Scottish Borders
J. Mercer, R. Buckland, P. Kirkland and J. Waddell. Atropos Publications (in press).

Useful addresses and web sites

Butterfly Conservation – Highland Branch, Scotland Office & UK National Office (for information see the reverse of the contents page).

Where to send your butterfly records
David Barbour, Highland butterfly recorder, 125a High Street, Aberlour, AB38 9PB. DbFIS@aol.com.

Web sites

www.butterfly-conservation.org
Butterfly Conservation main web site with links to Butterfly Conservation Scotland, local branches and the UK Butterfly Monitoring Scheme etc.

www.highland-butterflies.org.uk
The Highland Branch web site giving up to date information on what is going on in our area.

www.hbrg.org.uk
Highland Biological Recording Group – surveys and news of Highland wildlife and help with identification enquiries.

www.ukbutterflies.co.uk
Good for identification tips and links to other useful sites.

www.learnaboutbutterflies.com
Includes an excellent section on the butterfly life cycle.

www.whatsthatcaterpillar.co.uk
A good resource for identifying caterpillars of both butterflies and moths and you can send in your pictures for identification.

www.nbn.org.uk
National Biodiversity Network – maps and accounts of many insect species.